Reading STREET GEORGIA

Program Authors

Peter Afflerbach

Camille Blachowicz

Candy Dawson Boyd

Wendy Cheyney

Connie Juel

Edward Kame'enui

Donald Leu

Jeanne Paratore

P. David Pearson

Sam Sebesta

Deborah Simmons

Sharon Vaughn

Susan Watts-Taffe

Karen Kring Wixson

PEARSON

Scott Foresman

Editorial Offices: Glenview, Illinois • Parsippany, New Jersey • New York, New York
Sales Offices: Boston, Massachusetts • Duluth, Georgia • Glenview, Illinois
Coppell, Texas • Sacramento, California • Mesa, Arizona

We dedicate Reading Street to
Peter Jovanovich.

His wisdom, courage,
and passion for education
are an inspiration to us all.

About the Cover Artist
Daniel Moreton lives in New York City, where he uses his computer to create illustrations for books. He has two dogs—basset hounds named Zoey and Eddie. Can you find Eddie on the cover of this book?

ISBN-13: 978-0-328-42204-3
ISBN-10:   0-328-42204-5

2 3 4 5 6 7 8 9 10 V063 17 16 15 14 13 12 11 10 09

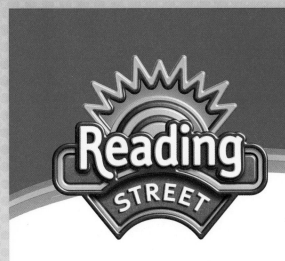

Dear Georgia Reader,

Scott Foresman Reading Street has many corners and crossroads. At each corner you will learn about something new and interesting. You will read about great ideas in science and social studies. You will have fun reading about clever chicks and smart mice detectives!

You may want to hurry down the street and read these wonderful stories and articles! But slow down, take your time, and enjoy yourself! You never know who you might meet on Reading Street!

Sincerely,
The Authors

Great Ideas

What difference can a great idea make?

Clever Solutions

Tippy-Toe Chick, GO!

Ideas That Changed the World

Great Ideas

What difference can a great idea make?

Tippy-Toe Chick, Go!

Little Chick solves a big problem.

ANIMAL FANTASY

connect to SOCIAL STUDIES

Mole and the Baby Bird

Grandfather helps Mole see his pet in a new way.

ANIMAL FANTASY

connect to SOCIAL STUDIES

Dot & Jabber and the Great Acorn Mystery

Dot and Jabber solve a science mystery.

INFORMATIONAL FICTION

connect to SCIENCE

Simple Machines

We learn how simple machines make our lives easier.

EXPOSITORY NONFICTION

connect to SCIENCE

Alexander Graham Bell

Alexander Graham Bell's invention improved how we communicate.

BIOGRAPHY

connect to SOCIAL STUDIES

Ben Franklin and His First Kite

One great idea can lead to another.

BIOGRAPHY

connect to SOCIAL STUDIES

9

Let's Talk About
Clever Solutions

Words to Read

along

behind

toward

eyes

never

pulling

Read the Words

The chicks walked along the path behind the house. They walked toward the garden. Their eyes popped open! They saw a big dog that they had never seen before. It was barking and pulling on its leash.

Tippy-Toe Chick, GO!

Genre: Animal Fantasy
The animal characters in an animal fantasy act like people. In the next story you will read about a smart little chick who surprises her family.

Tippy-Toe

by George Shannon
illustrated by Laura Dronzek

Chick, GO!

What great idea
will Little Chick have?

Every morning when the dew had dried, Hen took her chicks to the garden for their favorite treat—sweet itty-bitty beans and potato bugs.

Hen, Big Chick, and Middle Chick next, with Little Chick trailing along behind. Stopping to wonder at this and that.

Then running, *tippy-toe, tippy-toe,* to catch the rest. Across the yard. Into the garden to eat, eat, eat. Every day, every day of the week.

Till ONE day—

RUFF-RUFF-RUFF-RUFF-RUFF!

A big, grumpy dog came running their way, barking and growling at the end of a rope.

Hen jumped back and pulled her chicks near. "There's no safe way to the beans today. We'll just have to wait for chicken feed."

All three chicks said, "Bleck!" and frowned.

"We're hungry!"

"You PROMISED!"

"We DID our chores!"

Hen sighed. "But we'll NEVER get past a dog like that."

Big Chick said, "Wait. I'LL take care of this."
He slowly took a step toward Dog. "Now listen,"
he called. "We won't hurt you. We're just going
to the garden for an itty-bitty treat."

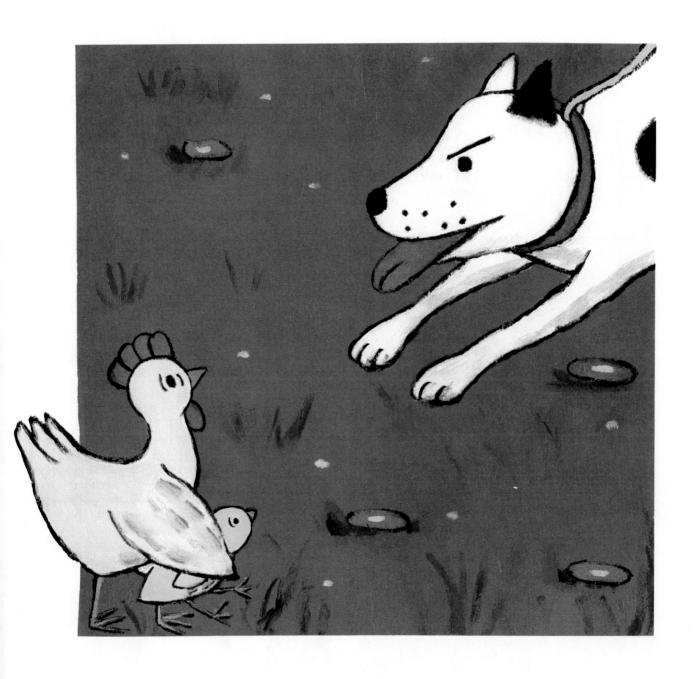

RUFF-RUFF-RUFF-RUFF-RUFF!

Dog disagreed, barking and pulling at the end of his rope. Big Chick ran to hide under Hen's safe wing.

Middle Chick took a breath, then stepped toward Dog. "I'M hungry, so YOU'D better stop it right now! Or YOU'LL be sorry when we get hold of you."

RUFF-RUFF-RUFF-RUFF-RUFF!

Dog disagreed, barking and pulling at the end
of his rope. Middle Chick ran to hide under
Hen's safe wing.

"Let's go," said Hen. "We'll really have to wait."

Little Chick peeped, "*I* want to try."

"Oh, no!" said Hen, as the other chicks laughed. "You're much too small."

Little Chick yelled, "But *I* can RUN!" And off she went, *tippy-toe, tippy-toe,* as fast as she could. Straight toward Dog.

Hen screamed and grabbed her heart.

Big Chick closed his eyes.

Middle Chick shook.

Little Chick ran, *tippy-toe, tippy-toe*, without
stopping to rest till she felt Dog's breath.

Then Little Chick laughed and began to run again. *Tippy-toe, tippy-toe* around the tree.

Dog chased after her, tugging at his rope.
RUFF-RUFF-RUFF-RUFF-RUFF!

Tippy-toe, tippy-toe around the tree. *Tippy-toe, tippy-toe, tippy* . . . **RUFF-RUFF-RUFF!**

Around and around, *tippy-toe, tippy-toe*. Till . . .

RUFF-RUP-yip-yip-yip-yip!
Dog's rope was wrapped all around the tree.
He was stuck and too mad to think "back up."

Hen clucked with pride. Big Chick and Middle
Chick just stood and stared.

Little Chick called, "It's time to eat!"

And off they ran, *tippy-toe, tippy-toe.* Right past Dog and into the garden for their favorite treat—sweet itty-bitty beans and potato bugs.

"YUM!"

Think and Share

Talk About It What would you say to Little Chick about her great idea?

1. The pictures below are mixed up. Decide in which order they belong. Then use them to retell the story. **Retell**

2. Where does Little Chick live? What words would you use to describe her? **Character/Setting**

3. How did the story begin? How did it end? **Story Structure**

Look Back and Write Why was Little Chick's idea great? Look at pages 28–31.

George Shannon

George Shannon is a tall man, but he likes little things. One of his favorite sayings is "Less is more." Does that sound like a good lesson for Little Chick?

Mr. Shannon likes to tell stories. He says, "I want my stories to sound as if they are being told out loud."

Read more books by George Shannon.

Belling the Cat

a fable adapted from Aesop
illustrated by Viviana Garofoli

The mice had a problem. There was a new cat in the house. It slept by the kitchen table. It hid behind doors. It raced down the hall toward the mice.

They could see its eyes in the dark.
They could hear it howl at night. They never
felt safe!

The mice called a meeting. They had many ideas.

One little mouse pulled on his ear and said, "We need to hear that cat. Let's hang a bell on its neck."

All the mice went along with the idea. They cheered and clapped. They danced and laughed.

Then a wise old mouse asked, "Who is going to bell the cat?"

Moral: Some things are easier said than done.

Advice

Prompt

Tippy-Toe Chick, Go! tells about a dog that barks and growls. Think about a dog that barks late at night.

Now write advice about ways to deal with this problem.

Writing Trait

Strong verbs give advice a **voice.**

Commands begin with strong verbs.

All commands are clear and short.

Student Model

Talk to the dog's owner.

Call neighbors for help.

Ask a vet for ideas.

Close your windows.

Turn up the TV.

Use earplugs.

Humor adds to <u>voice</u>.

GEORGIA Writing
For weekly writing in CRCT format, see the
Georgia Weekly CRCT Workbook, pages 173–176.

Writer's Checklist

✓ **Ideas** Do all sentences give advice?

✓ **Organization** Are the sentences in correct order?

✓ **Style** Do strong verbs tell readers what to do?

✓ **Conventions** Does every sentence begin with a capital letter and end with a period?

Grammar

Commands

A **command** is a sentence that tells someone to do something. It begins with a **capital letter.** It usually ends with a **period (.).**

Come back, Little Chick**.**
Please go away, Dog**.**

Look at the advice about the barking dog. Write another command that gives advice about what to do.

GEORGIA
Performance Standards **ELA1W1i.** Begins to write different types of sentences (e.g., simple/compound and declarative/interrogative). (Also **ELA1W1l.**)

43

Let's Talk About
Clever
Solutions

44

Words to Read

loved

wood

should

door

Read the Words

Mole loved the baby bird he found. He put it in a cage made of wood. What should Mole do? Should he keep the baby bird, or should he open the cage door and let the bird go?

Mole and the Baby Bird

Genre: Animal Fantasy
In an animal fantasy, the animal characters talk and act like people. The next story is about a mole who finds and takes care of a wild bird.

Mole and
the Baby Bird

by Marjorie Newman

illustrated by Patrick Benson

*What can Mole learn
from a baby bird?*

Mole found a baby bird.
It had fallen out of its nest.

Mole waited and waited: but no
big bird came to help it–so Mole
took the baby bird home.

He made a nest for it.
"Look!" he said to his mother.

"It's very, very hard to take care of a baby
bird," she said.

"They usually die," said his dad.

"My bird won't die," said Mole.

His friends helped him find food
for the baby.

His mother showed him how to feed it.
Mole fed it whenever it chirped.

And the bird didn't die! It grew.
"It's my pet bird," said Mole.
"It's not a pet bird. It's a wild bird,"
said his mother.

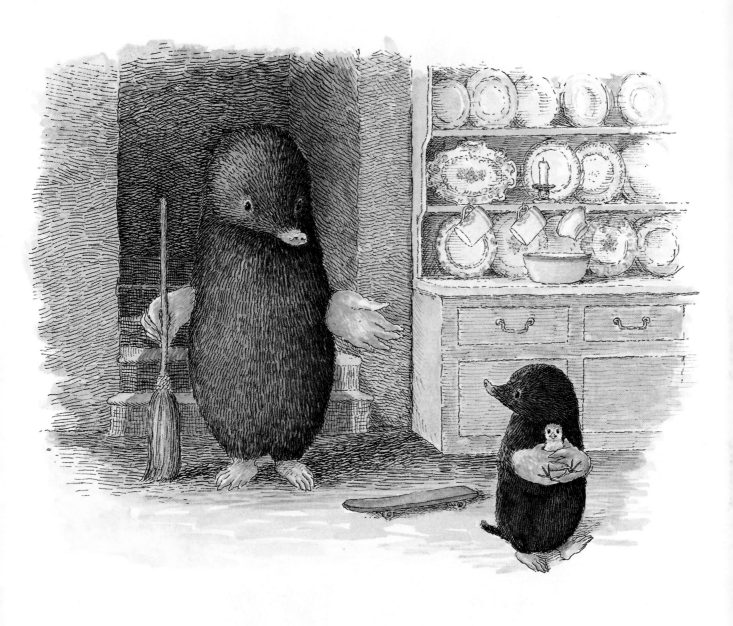

The bird fluttered its wings.

"Your bird is trying to fly," said his mother.

"No!" cried Mole. "It mustn't fly!"

Mole found some wood and some nails.
He borrowed his dad's toolbox.

"What are you making?" asked his dad.
"I'm making a cage for my pet bird!"
said Mole.

"It's not a pet bird. It's a wild bird,"
said his dad. "You should let it fly."
"No!" cried Mole.

He put his bird into its new cage.
The bird was sad.

Mole's mother was sad too. But Mole
kept his bird, because he loved it.

Then—Grandad came to visit. He looked at
Mole's pet bird.

Presently Grandad said, "Let's go for a walk,
little Mole."

Grandad took Mole to the top of a high hill.

Mole looked down at the trees far below.

He felt the wild wind trying to lift him.
"Wheee! I'm flying!" cried Mole.
"Nearly," said Grandad.

When Mole got home he looked at his bird.
It was sitting very still in its cage in Mole's dark
underground room. "Birds are meant to fly,"
said Mole.

He opened the cage door, and he let his bird
fly away because he loved it. Then he cried.

The next day Mole went into the forest.
He saw his bird flying, soaring, free. And Mole
was glad.

Think and Share

Talk About It What lesson did Mole learn? Was it a good lesson to learn? Why do you think so?

1. Use the pictures below to retell the story of *Mole and the Baby Bird.* Retell

2. Tell two things that happened after Mole found the baby bird. Sequence

3. How did Mole change at the end of the story? Character

Look Back and Write Mole tries to treat the baby bird like a pet. Look back at the story. What did he do? Make a list.

66

Marjorie Newman

Marjorie Newman lives in England. As a child, she often brought home caterpillars and tadpoles. When they turned into butterflies and frogs, she let them go.

Patrick Benson

Patrick Benson tries to show different views in his art. Can you find a picture that shows how the world looks to a flying bird?

Read another book written by Marjorie Newman or illustrated by Patrick Benson.

Dear Dr. Know-It-All

by Paulinda Lynk

Dear Dr. Know-It-All,
My sister never knocks on my door. She just barges into my room. What should I do?
Getting Mad

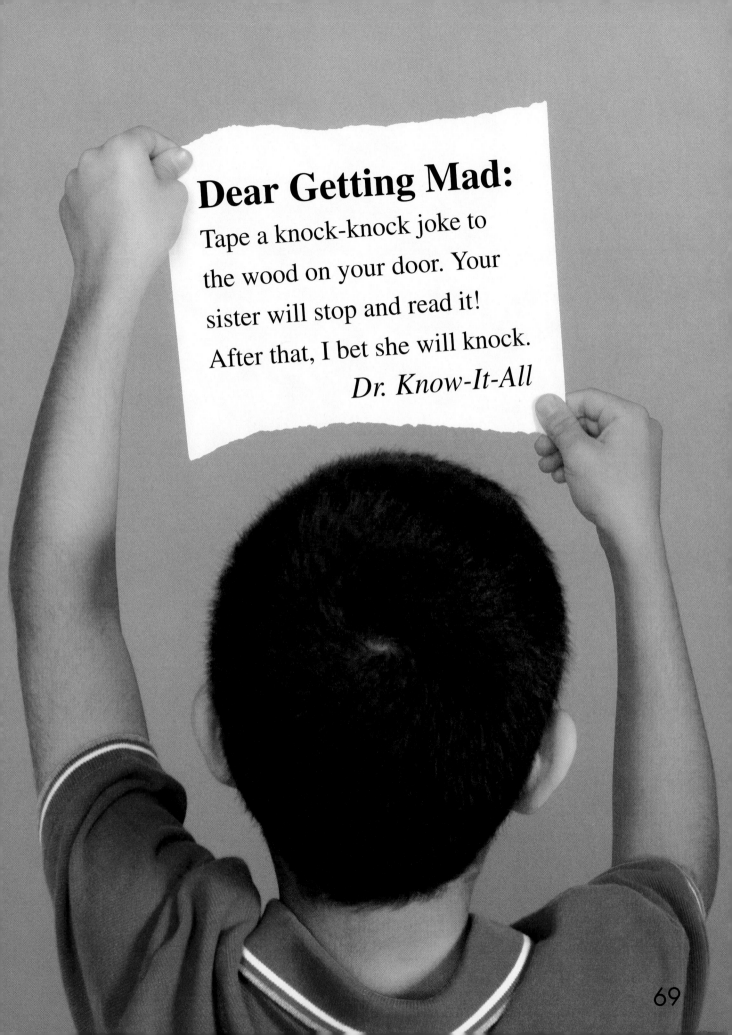

Dear Getting Mad:
Tape a knock-knock joke to the wood on your door. Your sister will stop and read it! After that, I bet she will knock.
Dr. Know-It-All

Dear Dr. Know-It-All,
I loved your idea!
And it worked.
I even found a book
of knock-knock jokes
to keep her knocking!
Not Mad Now

Knock-
Knock

Knock! Knock!
Who's There?
Boo.
Boo who?
Why are you crying?

71

More Knock-knock Jokes

Knock-knock.
Who's there?
Orange.
Orange who?
Orange you glad to see me?

Knock-knock.
Who's there?
Olive.
Olive who?
Olive to play with you!

Knock-knock.
Who's there?
Who.
Who who?
When did you get an owl?

Knock-knock.
Who's there?
Les.
Les who?
Les be friends!

Ending

Prompt

Mole and the Baby Bird teaches a lesson: Let wild animals be free.
Think about another story you know that teaches a lesson. Now write an ending that tells what lesson the story teaches.

Writing Trait

Conventions help readers understand your writing.

Student Model

One <u>convention</u> is capitalizing important words in title.

Story events are in order.

Story ends with lesson.

Ant and Grasshopper
All summer Ant works
hard and Grasshopper plays.
In winter Ant has food to
eat. Grasshopper has no
food at all! The lesson is to
plan for tomorrow.

GEORGIA · Writing

GEORGIA Writing

For weekly writing in CRCT format, see the
Georgia Weekly CRCT Workbook, pages 181–184.

Writer's Checklist

- ☑ **Ideas** Are all sentences about a story or its lesson?
- ☑ **Organization** Are story events in order? Is the lesson told at the end?
- ☑ **Style** Do story events help explain the lesson?
- ☑ **Conventions** Are words in the title correctly capitalized?

Grammar

Exclamations

An **exclamation** is a sentence that shows strong feeling. It begins with a **capital** letter. It ends with an **exclamation mark (!).**

The wild bird must not fly**!**

· ·

Look at the ending.
Write the exclamation.

GEORGIA
Performance Standards **ELA1W1i.** Begins to write different types of sentences (e.g., simple/compound and declarative/interrogative). (Also **ELA1W1l.**)

75

Let's Talk About
Clever
Solutions

	Taste	Touch	Smell	What is it?
Object 1	sour	bumpy		
Object 2				
Object 3				

?

Words to Read

among
instead
another
none

Read the Words

We looked outside. A squirrel found an acorn among the leaves. He didn't eat it. Instead, he dug a hole and put the acorn in it. Then the squirrel found another acorn. None of us saw where he put that one.

Dot & Jabber
and the Great Acorn Mystery

Genre: Informational Fiction
Informational fiction tells a make-believe story, but it also gives facts and information that are true. The next story is a mystery about trees and how they grow where they do.

Dot & Jabber
and the Great Acorn Mystery

by Ellen Stoll Walsh

How will Dot and Jabber

solve this mystery?

81

The detectives had nothing to do.

"We need a mystery to solve," said Jabber.

"Here's a mystery," said Dot. "What is this little oak tree doing here?"

"Why is that a mystery?" Jabber wanted
to know.

"Because of the acorn," said Dot. "How did
it get here?"

"Dot," said Jabber, "what acorn?"

"Acorns are oak tree seeds. This little oak tree grew from an acorn, and acorns come from big oak trees."

"Oh, *that* acorn," said Jabber. "But where's the big oak tree?"

"That's part of the mystery," said Dot. "Let's look for clues."

"Okay!" shouted Jabber. "Because we're detectives!" He poked his head into a hole.

"Hey, this is *my* hole," said a mole. "Go away. There are no clues down here. Try the big oak tree—on the *other* side of the meadow."

"Of course!" said Dot. "Come on, Jabber!"

"That's a long, long way," said Jabber.
"How did our acorn get from there to here?
Do you think it walked?"

"Let's find out," said Dot. "The acorn began at the big oak tree. So will we."

The detectives set off across the meadow.

After a while Jabber said, "I'm tired. Can we wonder about all these maple seeds instead?"

"There's no mystery in maple seeds," said Dot. "They have wings that twirl, and they ride the wind across the meadow."

"Maybe our acorn rode the wind too,"
said Jabber.

"That is what we are going to find out,"
said Dot.

At last they arrived at the big oak tree. "Look!" said Dot. "I bet there are a million acorns here."

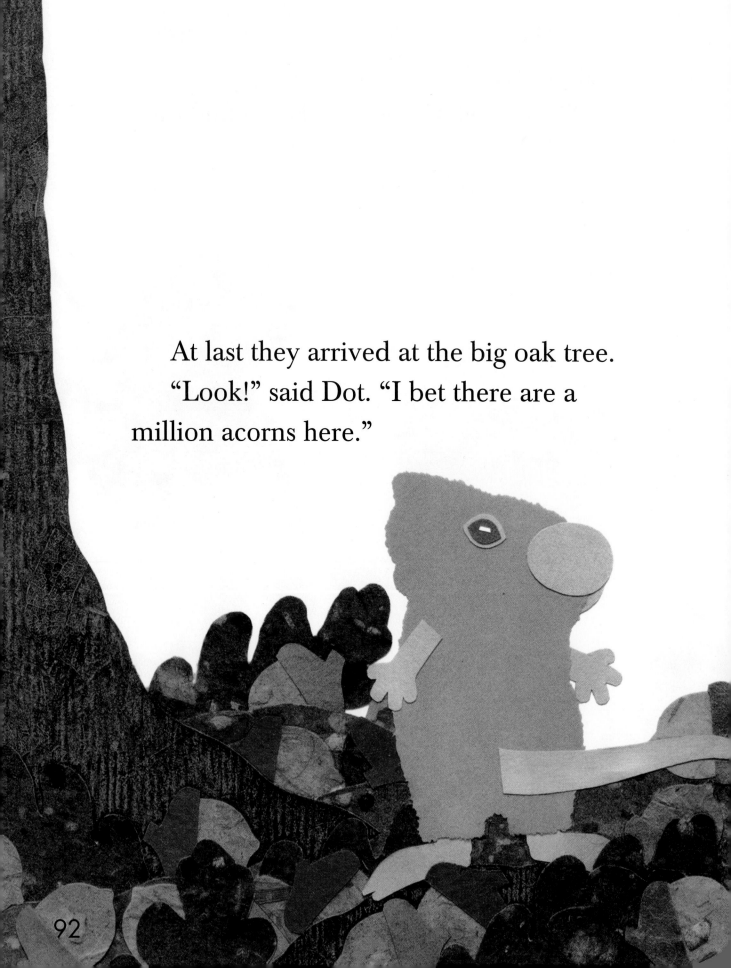

"They don't have wings," said Jabber.
"But they taste good."
"Don't eat them, Jabber! They're clues."

"Acorns don't have wings, but they might have sneaky feet," said Dot. "Let's keep watch and see if they start to move."

Plip. An acorn dropped from the big oak tree.

Jabber poked it with a stick. "This acorn isn't going anywhere," he said. "None of them are."

A squirrel came and sat down among
the acorns.

"Jabber, look!" Dot whispered. "What is
he doing?"

"Oh!" gasped Jabber. "He's eating our clue!"

"He can't be," said Dot. "The shell is still
on it."

"So why is he stuffing it in his mouth?" asked Jabber.

The squirrel ran off.

"Oh no, he's stealing the acorn!" the detectives cried and ran after him.

When the squirrel stopped, they stopped and watched to see what would happen next.

"What's he doing now?" asked Jabber.

"Digging a hole. Look! He's hiding the acorn."

Jabber stared at Dot. "Maybe he's planting it!"

"Of course!" said Dot. "Our acorn crossed the meadow on squirrel feet."

"And got planted by squirrel feet," said Jabber.

"And grew into the little oak tree," said Dot. "The mystery is solved. We are two clever mouse detectives!"

"Hurray!" shouted Jabber. "Now what will we do?"

"Find another mystery," said Dot.

"But I'm hungry," said Jabber. "First let's go eat some of those leftover clues."

Think and Share

Talk About It What makes Dot and Jabber good detectives?

1. Use the pictures below to summarize what you learned about seeds. **Retell**

2. How are acorns different from maple tree seeds? **Compare/Contrast**

3. Did you reread parts of the story? How did that help? **Fix Up**

Look Back and Write What was the answer to the great acorn mystery? Look back at page 99.

Ellen Stoll Walsh

Ellen Stoll Walsh grew up in a big family. She was one of ten children! It was fun but noisy. She liked to read books to get away from the noise.

Now Ms. Walsh writes books. She cuts paper to make the art. In her books, she tells stories and teaches facts about the world.

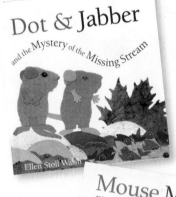

Read more books by Ellen Stoll Walsh.

Water

Our class did an experiment. We observed changes in water. Here's what we did.

1. We put water in a cup.
2. We marked it with a line.
3. We waited one week.
4. We took notes.

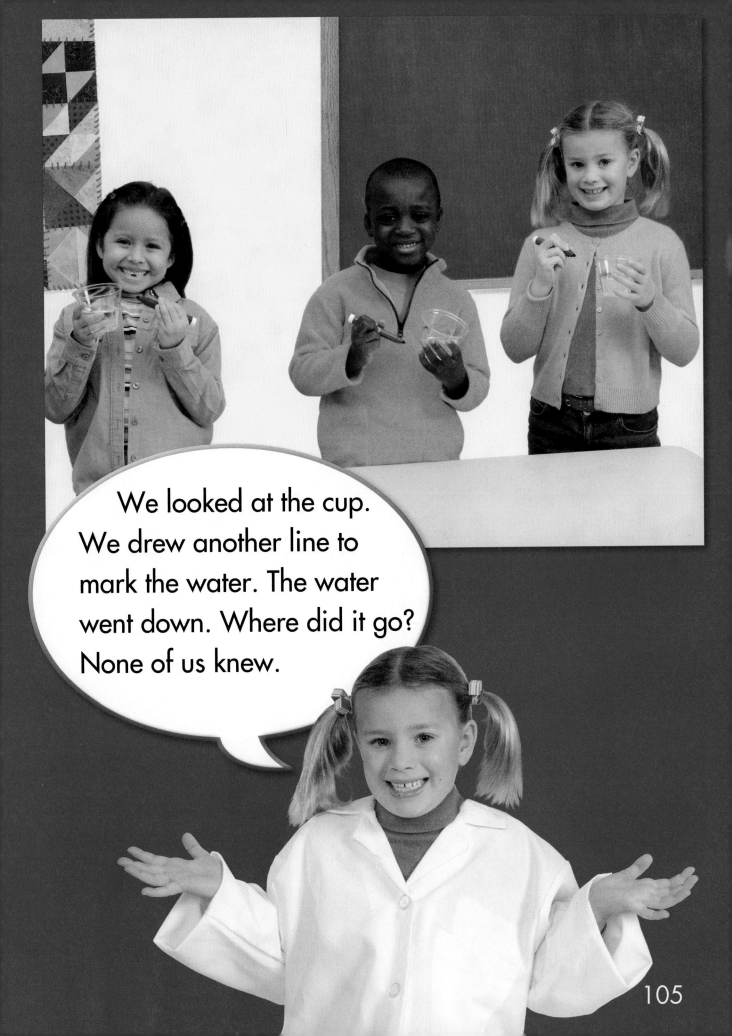

We looked at the cup. We drew another line to mark the water. The water went down. Where did it go? None of us knew.

Our teacher said that the water went into the air. It is there, but we can't see it. This is called evaporation.

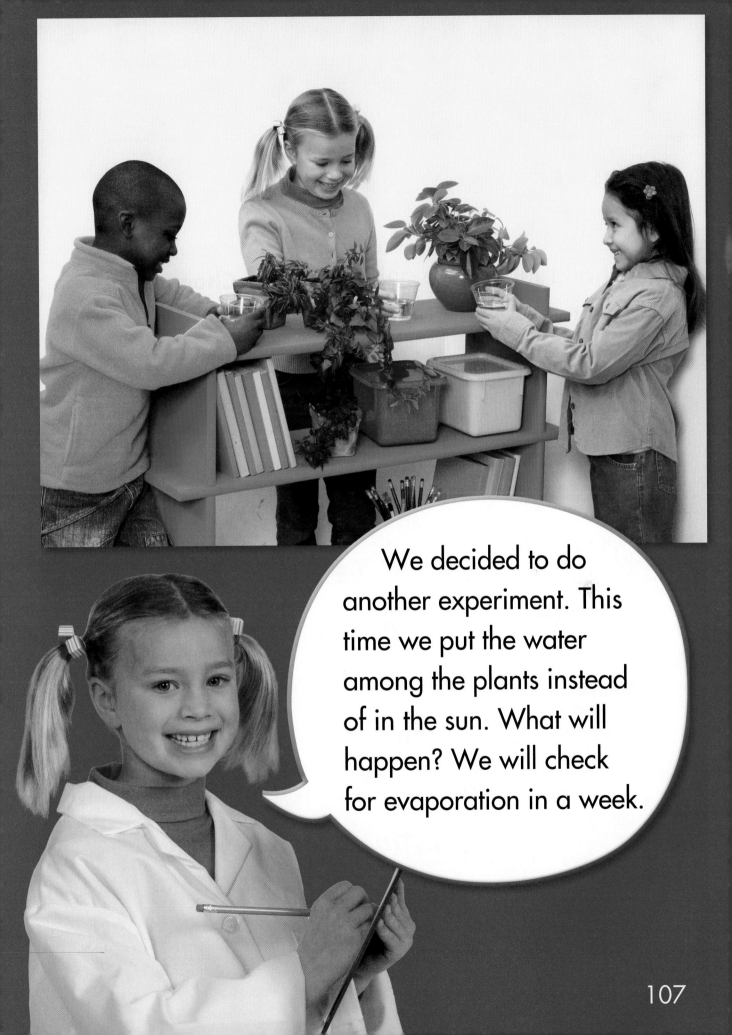

We decided to do another experiment. This time we put the water among the plants instead of in the sun. What will happen? We will check for evaporation in a week.

Answer

Prompt

Dot and Jabber are animal detectives. Think about this question: What do good detectives do? Now write the question and sentences that answer it.

Writing Trait

Choose exact **words** for your answers.

Student Model

Question is first.

Sentences answer question.

> Word
> choice
> makes
> answers
> clear.

What do good detectives do? Good detectives look for clues. They take notes and pictures. They ask questions. They figure out what happened. Good detectives solve mysteries!

GEORGIA Writing

For weekly writing in CRCT format, see the *Georgia Weekly CRCT Workbook*, pages 189–192.

GEORGIA • Writing

Writer's Checklist

☑ **Ideas** Do all sentences answer the question?

☑ **Organization** Do sentences build to an end?

☑ **Style** Do exact words make answers clear?

☑ **Conventions** Do sentences begin with a capital letter and have the correct end mark?

Grammar

How Sentences Begin and End

A **sentence** is a group of words that tells a complete idea. It begins with a **capital letter**. A **statement** ends with a **period (.)**. A question ends with a **question mark (?)**.

Acorns are oak tree seeds**.**

How did this oak tree get here**?**

• •

Look at answers to the question. Write one of the statements as a question.

GEORGIA

Performance Standards **ELA1W1i.** Uses appropriate end punctuation (period and question mark) and correct capitalization of initial words and common proper nouns (e.g., personal names, months). (Also **ELA1W1i.**)

109

Let's Talk About

Ideas That Changed the World

Words to Read

goes
kinds
heavy
against
today

Read the Words

The forklift goes back and forth. It lifts all kinds of heavy boxes. It stacks them against the wall. The boxes will be shipped today.

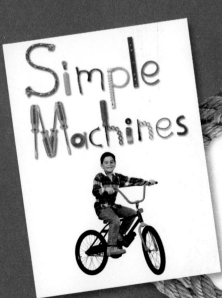

Genre: Expository Nonfiction
Expository nonfiction explains something. The next selection explains how simple machines make work easier.

Simple Machines

by Allan Fowler

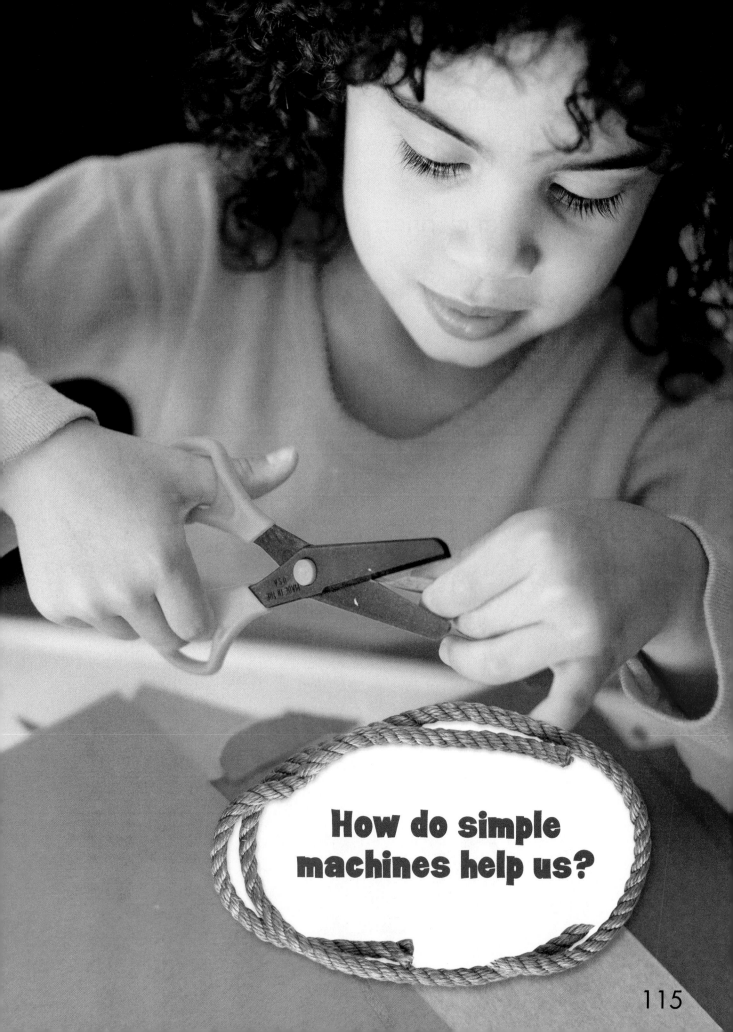

How do simple machines help us?

We use machines every day. Machines help make our lives easier.

Some machines, such as lawn mowers and vacuum cleaners, have many parts.

vacuum cleaner

lawn mower

Other machines have few parts. They are called simple machines. Levers, inclined planes, wheels and axles, and pulleys are four kinds of simple machines.

These everyday things are simple machines.

This bottle opener is a kind of lever.
It helps you remove the cap from a bottle.

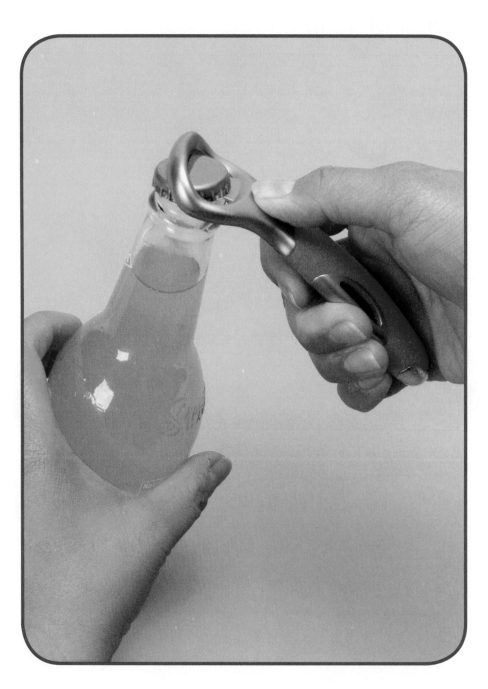

Some levers can help you move a heavy object, such as a rock.

This boy is using a lever called a crowbar.

Push down on one end of a lever. The other end moves up and pushes against whatever you are trying to move.

Have you ever ridden a seesaw?

A seesaw is a kind of lever. One side
goes up, while the other side goes down.

Inclined planes are all around you.

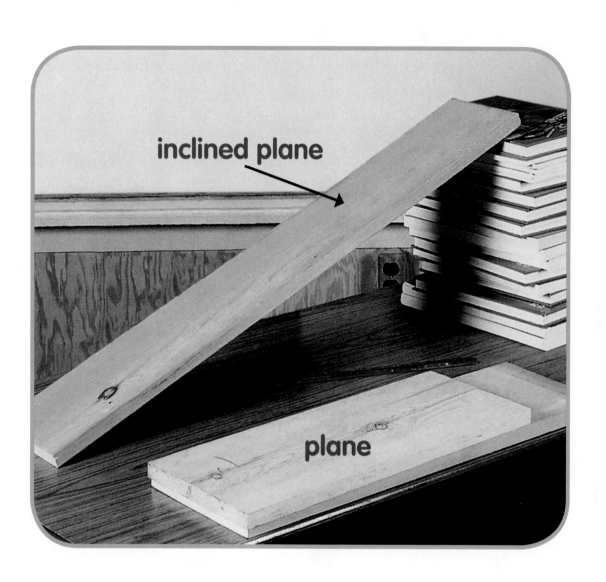

inclined plane

plane

A plane is just a flat surface, like a wooden board. An inclined plane is a flat surface that is slanted.

Ramps are inclined planes. It is easier to push a big load up a ramp than to lift it.

A wedge is another kind of inclined plane.

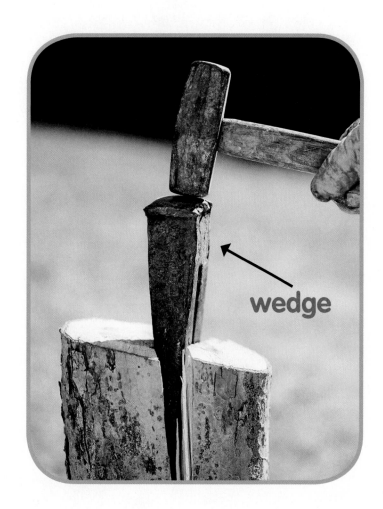

wedge

A wedge can help you cut wood.
When a wedge is hit with a big
hammer, its thin part splits the wood.

Wheels help things go.

axle

An axle, or rod, connects a pair of wheels. The axle helps the wheels turn.

Wheels are on bicycles and cars. It would be very hard to move a bike or car without wheels.

A pulley helps you lift heavy objects.

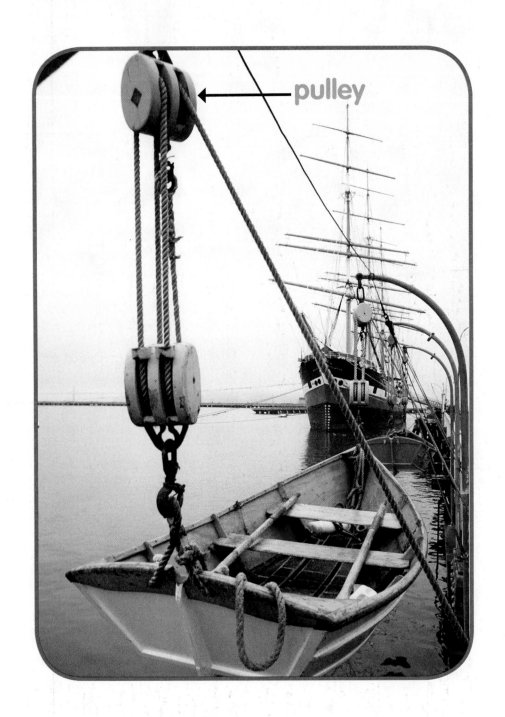

pulley

A pulley's rope passes over a small wheel.
Pull down on one end of the rope. You can lift
a very heavy load tied to the other end.

A pulley can help you raise and lower the flag on a flagpole.

You can even lift the sail on a boat using a pulley.

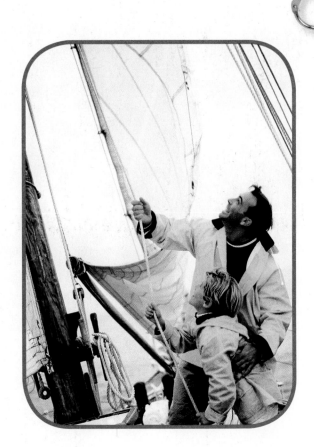

129

These children are using two kinds of simple machines. A wheelbarrow is a kind of lever, and it has wheels.

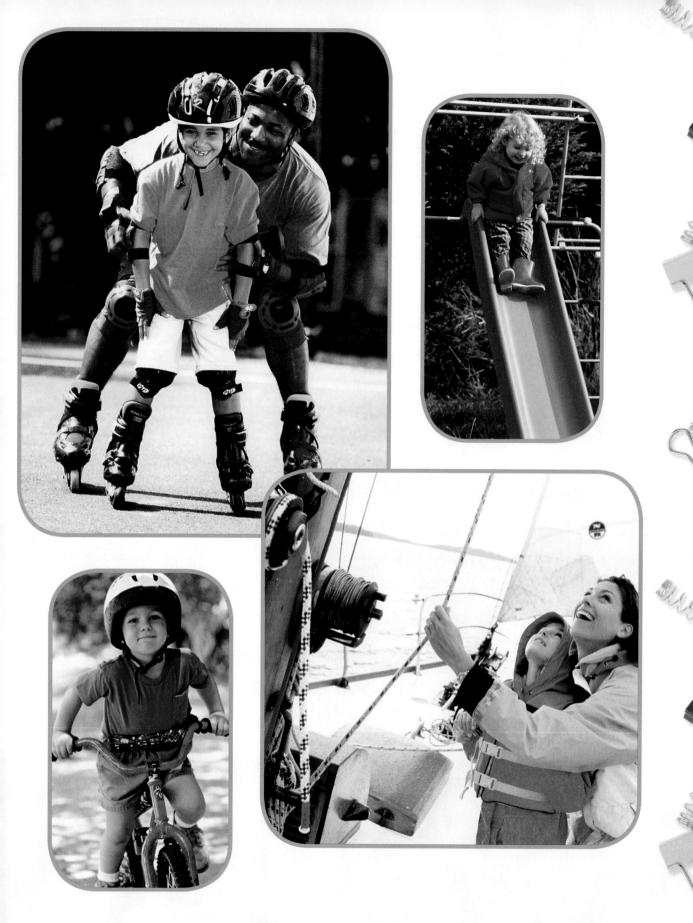

Have you used any simple machines today?

Think and Share

Talk About It Machines can be very simple. Talk about simple machines you use in the classroom.

1. Use the pictures below to summarize what you learned. **Retell**

2. What is this selection mostly about? **Main Idea**

3. Did you stop to sum up after you read about levers before reading on? How did that help you? **Summarize**

Look Back and Write How would you get an inclined plane to help you get a big box onto a truck? Look back at page 124.

Meet the Author
Allan Fowler

Allan Fowler has written many science books for beginning readers. He likes to travel and write about different parts of the world.

Mr. Fowler was born in New York, but he lives in Chicago now. He worked in advertising before he became a writer.

Read more books by Allan Fowler.

Roy's Wheelchair

by Callen Watkins

Roy uses a wheelchair. It has axles and wheels. He goes all around town with it.

Today Roy is going to the toy store.
He uses the ramp to get to the door.

The door is heavy. He pushes
against the opener to get in.

Roy uses his wheelchair to do all kinds of things!

Writing and Grammar

Explanation

Prompt

Simple Machines explains how simple machines work. Think about a modern machine. Now write an explanation telling how the machine makes life easier.

Writing Trait

Organize ideas so your explanation is clear.

Student Model

Machine is named at beginning.

Main idea sentence is first in order.

Each supporting sentence states one reason.

Refrigerators are useful machines. They keep food cold and fresh. Food would spoil quickly without refrigerators. A refrigerator saves money because it stops waste.

GEORGIA • Writing

GEORGIA Writing

For weekly writing in CRCT format, see the
Georgia Weekly CRCT Workbook, pages 197–200.

Writer's Checklist

- ✓ **Ideas** Do all sentences tell about a machine?
- ✓ **Organization** Is the main idea stated first?
- ✓ **Style** Do details support the main idea?
- ✓ **Conventions** Are pronouns used correctly?

Grammar

Pronouns

A **pronoun** is a word that takes the place of a noun or nouns. The words **he, she, it, I, we, you,** and **they** are pronouns.

The ramp is ready. **It** is ready.
Tess and I walk up. **We** walk up.

• •

Look at the explanation. Write two different pronouns. Write the noun that each pronoun replaces.

GEORGIA
Performance Standards **ELA1W1g.** Begins to use personal pronouns (e.g., I, me, we, us) in place of nouns.
GPS (Also **ELA1W1a.**)

139

Let's Talk About
Ideas That Changed the World

140

Words to Read

early
learn
science
built
through

142

Read the Words

Early in life, a man named Mr. Bell liked to learn about science. He later built a machine that sent voices through wires. Do you know the name of that machine?

Alexander Graham Bell

Genre: Biography
A biography tells a person's life story. It is written by someone else. Now you will read about the man who invented the telephone, Alexander Graham Bell.

Alexander Graham Bell

by Lola M. Schaefer

Why is Alexander Graham Bell an important person to know?

Alexander Graham Bell was born in Scotland in 1847. His father was a famous teacher who taught people how to speak well.

 Time line

born

1847

Scotland

Alexander's mother was deaf. She was still able to teach him to play the piano. Alexander was good at music and science.

 Time line

born

1847

**The Bell Family
Alexander is on the left.**

Alexander was interested in sound. He also liked to invent things. He built a machine that could speak. He also tried to make his dog talk.

Time line

born

1847

**Alexander using
an early invention**

In 1871, Alexander moved to Boston. During the day, he taught deaf students how to speak. At night, he did experiments with sound.

Time line

born

teaches deaf
students in
Boston

1847 — **1871**

**Classroom at a school
for the deaf**

Alexander wanted to learn more about electricity. In 1874, he met Tom Watson. Tom knew how electricity worked. They began to work together.

Time line

born

teaches deaf students in Boston

begins work with Tom Watson

1847 — **1871** — **1874** —

**Electricity can make sound
travel through wires.**

Alexander stopped teaching. He did experiments day and night. He and Tom wanted to invent a machine that could send voices from one place to another.

Time line

born

teaches deaf students in Boston

begins work with Tom Watson

1847 — **1871** — **1874**

THIS MODEL OF BELL'S FIRST
TELEPHONE IS A DUPLICATE OF THE INSTRU-
MENT THROUGH WHICH SPEECH SOUNDS WERE
FIRST TRANSMITTED ELECTRICALLY. 1875.

**A model of Bell's
first telephone**

On March 10, 1876, Alexander and Tom reached their goal. Alexander spoke to Tom through the first telephone.

 Time line

born

teaches deaf students in Boston

begins work with Tom Watson

1847 — **1871** — **1874** —

**Alexander Graham Bell
using his telephone**

invents
telephone with
Tom Watson

1876

Alexander and Tom made the telephone better. Soon it could send voices many miles. In 1915, they made the first telephone call across the United States.

 Time line

born
1847

teaches deaf students in Boston
1871

begins work with Tom Watson
1874

The first telephone call
across the United States

invents telephone with Tom Watson

makes first telephone call across the United States

1876 — **1915**

Alexander spent his life inventing. He died in 1922. Alexander Graham Bell changed the way people communicate with one another.

Time line

born
1847

teaches deaf students in Boston
1871

begins work with Tom Watson
1874

invents telephone with Tom Watson

makes first telephone call across the United States

dies

1876 — **1915** **1922** —

Think and Share

Talk About It What would you say to thank Mr. Alexander Graham Bell for what he did?

1. Use the pictures below to summarize Mr. Bell's life and work. **Retell**

2. Describe the kind of person Alexander Graham Bell was. **Draw Conclusions**

3. How does the time line help you understand Mr. Bell and his life? **Text Features**

Look Back and Write Look back at page 150. What fantastic thing did Mr. Bell try to do? What do you think happened?

Meet the Author
Lola M. Schaefer

As a child, Lola Schaefer loved to read. "I read every biography in our school library," she says. Now she writes biographies for beginning readers.

Ms. Schaefer says, "Whenever you read a good book, pass it to a friend. Then the two of you can talk about your favorite parts."

Read more books by Lola M. Schaefer.

Inventions

THE **HISTORY** OF **INVENTION**

Maude likes science. She wants to learn more about inventions. So she visits an Internet Web site called The History of Invention. Here's what she sees.

Maude clicks on a picture to learn more.

File   Edit   View   Favorites   Tools   Help

Sliced bread, invented in 1928

Maude reads about early inventions like eyeglasses and the first airplane ever built. She learns about inventions all through history—even the invention of sliced bread.

Write Now

Writing and Grammar

List

Prompt

Alexander Graham Bell tells about some of Bell's inventions. Think about useful inventions. Now write a list of the inventions and tell how each one is useful.

Writing Trait

The items on this list should **focus** on one main **idea**.

Each sentence names an invention and tells how it is used.

I and *me* are used correctly.

Sentences <u>focus</u> on the prompt.

Student Model

We do homework on computers.

I find facts on the Internet.

Microwave ovens cook food fast.

Friends talk on telephones.

Planes take me many places.

168

For weekly writing in CRCT format, see the
Georgia Weekly CRCT Workbook, pages 205–208.

Writer's Checklist

✓ **Ideas** Are all sentences about inventions?

✓ **Organization** Are sentences written in a list?

✓ **Style** Do I tell how inventions are helpful?

✓ **Conventions** Is the pronoun *I* capitalized?

Grammar

Using I and Me

The pronouns **I** and **me** take the place
of your name. Use **I** in the subject of a
sentence. Use **me** after an action verb.
Always write **I** with a capital letter.

I invent things. Vin helps **me.**

When you talk about yourself and another
person, name yourself last: Al and **I** work.

· ·

Write two sentences about something
you like to eat. Use **I** and **me.**

GEORGIA
Performance Standards   **ELA1W1g.** Begins to use personal pronouns (e.g., I, me, we, us) in place of nouns.
(Also **ELA1W1a.**)

GPS

169

Let's Talk About

Ideas That Changed the World

Words to Read

| brothers |
| answered |
| poor |
| carry |
| different |

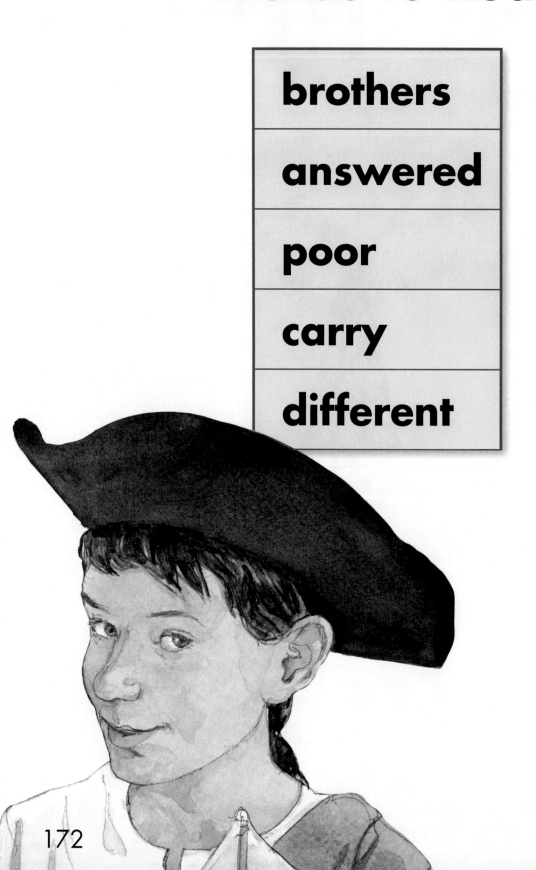

172

Read the Words

"How many brothers did Ben Franklin have?" asked Kenji.

"I don't know," answered Carlos, "but I read that his family was poor."

"He liked to carry out many different experiments," added Kate.

Genre: Biography
A biography sometimes tells about only a small part of a person's life. Next you will read about Ben Franklin when he was a boy.

Ben Franklin
and His First Kite

written by Stephen Krensky

illustrated by Bert Dodson

What will Ben do
with his kite?

Ten-year-old Benjamin Franklin was hard at work in his father's candle shop. He was cutting wicks. He carefully laid out each one.

Ben stretched his arms and let out a yawn. Candles could be tall or short, fat or thin, and even different colors. But there was nothing fun about candles for Ben.

"When do you think we'll be done today?"
Ben asked his father.

"Soon enough," his father answered.
"Why? Do you have special plans?"

Ben's father smiled. It was a rare day indeed when Ben did not have a plan in mind.

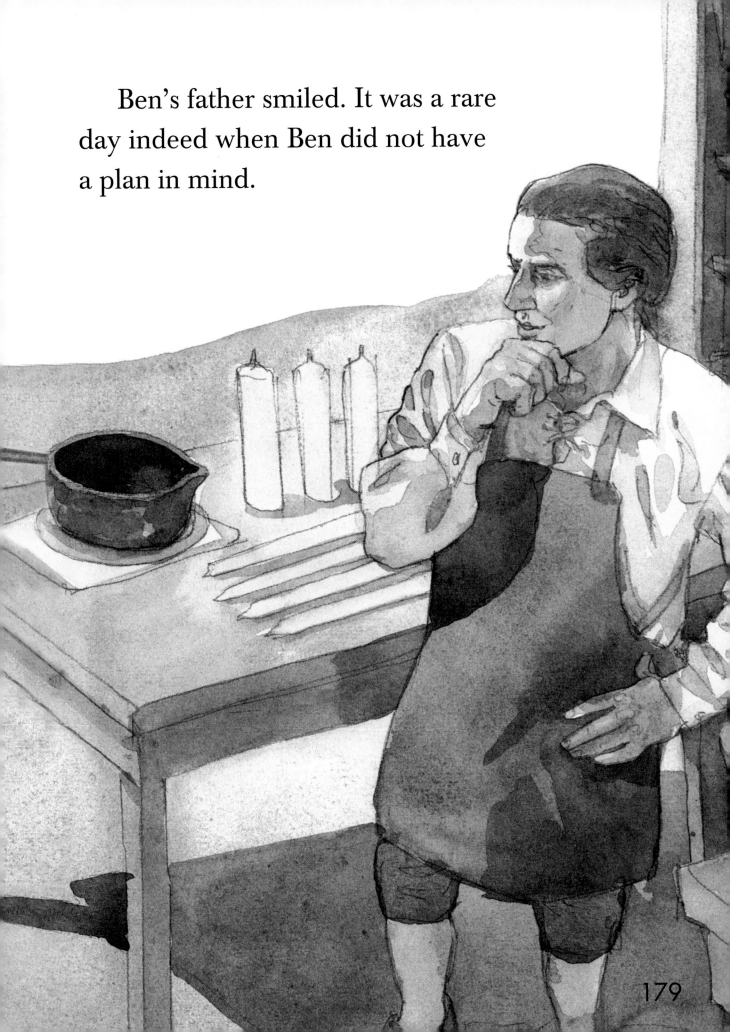

"Yes," said Ben. "I want to try an experiment at the millpond."

"You'll be swimming, then?" his father asked.

Ben grinned. "Partly," he said.

His father nodded. Ben was a fine swimmer.

That afternoon Ben flew down the streets of Boston. He was headed for home. Along the way he noticed the waves cresting in the harbor. The ships rocked back and forth. That was good, he thought. He needed a strong wind today.

When Ben got to his house, his mother met him at the door. Inside, two of his sisters were busy making hasty pudding by the hearth. Ben had sixteen brothers and sisters.

"Ben," his mother said, "why are you in such a hurry?"

Ben told her about his plan.

"Since your father approves, I won't keep you," said his mother. "Just be back for supper."

Ben nodded. He ran to get the kite he had made the week before. Then he left the house.

At the millpond a few of Ben's friends had arrived to watch.

"You've picked a poor place to fly a kite," said one.

Ben shrugged. "I'm doing an experiment," he said.

Ben got undressed. He gave his clothes to one of his friends.

"Please carry these to the other side of the pond," he said.

"What are you going to do?" asked the other boys. "Carry the kite while you swim?"

"No," said Ben. "The kite is going to carry me."

"But that kite is nothing special. It's just paper, sticks, and string," said one boy.

"That's true," Ben said. "But you see, the kite isn't the invention. The invention is what I'm going to do with it."

Ben raised the kite in the air. Once the wind had caught and carried it aloft, Ben walked into the water. There he lay on his back, floating.

"I'm going to cross this pond without swimming a stroke," said Ben.

The wind tugged on the kite.
The kite string tightened. The
water began to ripple at Ben's
feet. The kite was pulling him!

189

The boys whooped and hollered
as Ben glided across the pond. Finally
he reached the other side. The other
boys met him there.

"That was amazing!" said one.

"You crossed the whole pond without
swimming a stroke," said another.

"What will you do next?" they asked.
"Another invention? A different experiment?"
Ben didn't know. But he was sure he would think of something.

Ben's Great

Ben Franklin

Benjamin Franklin proved that lightning is electricity.

Franklin invented lightning rods. They are put on houses to prevent fires caused by lightning.

194

Ideas

Chair with ladder

Bifocal glasses

Franklin stove

Think and Share

Talk About It Would you like to have been a friend of Ben Franklin's? Explain.

1. Decide in which order the pictures belong. Use them to retell Ben's story.
Retell

2. What did you learn about great ideas from reading this biography? **Theme**

3. What questions did you ask yourself as you read this selection? How did that help you with your reading? **Ask Questions**

Look Back and Write Why was a strong wind important to Ben on this day? Look back at page 189 to help you answer.

Meet the Author
Stephen Krensky

Stephen Krensky is the author of over seventy books for children! He says, "Writing is hard and fun at the same time."

As a boy Mr. Krensky liked to make up stories. He would pretend he was in big adventures. Today he lives in Massachusetts with his wife and two sons, Andrew and Peter.

Read more books by Stephen Krensky.

I Made a Mechanical Dragon

by Jack Prelutsky
illustrated by Peter Sis

I made a mechanical dragon
Of bottle tops, hinges, and strings,
Of thrown-away clocks and unmendable socks,
Of hangers and worn innersprings.
I built it of cardboard and plastic,
Of doorknobs and cables and corks,
Of spools and balloons and unusable spoons,
And rusty old hinges and forks.

It's quite an unusual dragon
It rolls on irregular wheels,
It clatters and creaks and it rattles and squeaks,
And when it tips over, it squeals.
I've tried to control its maneuvers,
It fails to obey my commands,
It bumps into walls till it totters and falls—
I made it myself with my hands!

Lighthouse

LIG

by Joan Bransfield Graham
illustrated by Nancy Davis

HT LIGHT

LIGHT

Oh, Captain of the midnight sky, you stretch your arms and flash your eye across the waves and churning foam to steer me, guide me, safely HOME.

LIGHT HOUSE

Plan

Prompt

In *Ben Franklin and His First Kite*, Ben the inventor had a plan. Think about an invention you would like to make. Now write a plan telling what your invention can do.

Writing Trait

Sentences in a plan are usually statements.

Student Model

First sentence introduces invention.

Writer uses strong verbs.

Sentences are statements about invention.

I will invent Homework Helper.

You can ask it any question.

It solves math problems.

It finds information fast.

You will have a smart friend anytime.

GEORGIA · Writing

GEORGIA Writing
For weekly writing in CRCT format, see the
Georgia Weekly CRCT Workbook, pages 213–216.

Writer's Checklist

✔ **Ideas** Are all sentences about a new invention?

✔ **Organization** Does the sentence order make sense?

✔ **Style** Do details tell what the invention does?

✔ **Conventions** Are sentences punctuated correctly?

Grammar

More About Pronouns

A **pronoun** takes the place of some words in a sentence. **I, you, he, she, it, we,** and **they** are used in the **naming part** of a sentence. **Me, you, him, her, it, us,** and **them** are used in the **action part.**

Ben made a **kite**. **He** made **it.**

· ·

Look at the plan. Write the sentence that has a pronoun in the naming part and another pronoun in the action part.

GEORGIA
Performance Standards **ELA1W1g.** Begins to use personal pronouns (e.g., I, me, we, us) in place of nouns.
GPS (Also **ELA1W1a.**)

203

Wrap-Up

What's the Big Idea?

connect to
WRITING

Look around your home and school. Find a machine or another idea that makes a big difference in your life. Draw a picture of it. Write how it changes your life.

The Best Idea

connect to **DRAMA**

What was the best idea you read about in this unit? Choose the story that tells about the best idea. Act out the story with a friend. Tell how the idea makes a difference.

A Good Result

connect to **SOCIAL STUDIES**

Mole did not want his bird to fly. Then Grandad changed Mole's mind. Think about a time you changed your mind. Why was that a good idea? Talk it over with a partner.

Glossary

Aa   **amazing** Something that is **amazing** is very surprising. The hero made an **amazing** escape.

axles **Axles** are bars on which wheels turn.

axle

Bb   **borrowed** If you **borrowed** something, you got it from a person or a place just for a while. I **borrowed** books from the library.

Boston **Boston** is the capital city of Massachusetts, which is a state in the United States.

breath **Breath** is air taken into and sent out of the lungs. Take a deep **breath.**

Cc

communicate To **communicate** is to give and take news and information.

Dd

detectives **Detectives** are police officers or other people who work at solving mysteries.

disagreed If you and a friend **disagreed,** that means both had different ideas.

disagreed

207

Ee

electricity **Electricity** is a kind of energy that makes light and heat. **Electricity** also runs motors. **Electricity** makes light bulbs shine, radios and televisions play, and cars start.

Ff

famous A **famous** person is one who is well-known and important. The **famous** singer was met by a large crowd.

favorite Your **favorite** thing is the one you like better than all the others. What is your **favorite** flower?

Hh

harbor A **harbor** is an area of water where ships are safe. The boat sailed for the **harbor** when the storm began.

harbor

hearth

hasty pudding **Hasty pudding** is mush made of cornmeal.

hearth A **hearth** is the stone or brick floor of a fireplace.

hey **Hey** is a sound you make to get someone's attention.

hurray **Hurray** is what you shout when you are very happy. Give a **hurray** for our team!

209

Ii

inclined plane An **inclined plane** is a plank or other flat surface placed at an angle and used to move heavy things to a higher place. It is a simple machine.

inclined plane

invention An **invention** is a new thing that someone makes or thinks of. The light bulb was a wonderful **invention.**

Ll

lawn A **lawn** is a piece of land that is covered with grass and near a house. The grass of a **lawn** is usually kept short.

Mm

machines **Machines** are things with moving parts that do work for you. Cars, washers, and computers are **machines.**

meadow

meadow A **meadow** is a piece of land where grass grows. There are sheep in the **meadow.**

million A **million** is a very large number. It is also written 1,000,000.

mystery A **mystery** is something that is hard to understand. It was a **mystery** why the radio started playing in the middle of the night.

Pp

piano A **piano** is a large musical instrument that you sit at and play with your fingers.

potato bug

potato bugs **Potato bugs** are beetles that eat the leaves of the potato plant.

presently **Presently** means at the present time, or now. She is **presently** in first grade.

pulleys **Pulleys** are wheels with ropes that help lift things.

pulley

Ss

Scotland **Scotland** is a country north of England.

solve When you **solve** something, you find the answer to it. The detective will **solve** the mystery by using the clues.

solved **Solved** is the past tense of solve.

surface A **surface** is the top part or outside of something. The **surface** of the road was very wet after the rain.

surface

Tt

telephone A **telephone** is something you use to talk to people far away. Please answer the **telephone** if it rings.

telephone

tippy-toe **Tippy-toe** means on the tips of your toes. The girl walked **tippy-toe** so that she would not wake her baby brother.

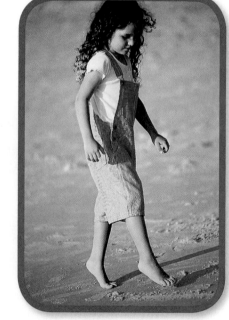

tippy-toe

Uu   **usually** If something **usually** happens, it happens very often or almost all the time. We **usually** eat dinner at six o'clock.

Vv   **vacuum** A **vacuum** cleaner is a machine you can use to clean rugs, curtains, and floors.

vacuum

Tippy-Toe Chick, Go!

along
behind
eyes
never
pulling
toward

Mole and the Baby Bird

door
loved
should
wood

Dot & Jabber and the Great Acorn Mystery

among
another
instead
none

Simple Machines

against
goes
heavy
kinds
today

Tested Words

Alexander Graham Bell

built
early
learn
science
through

Ben Franklin and His First Kite

answered
brothers
carry
different
poor

Acknowledgments

Text

Page 14: *Tippy-Toe Chick, Go!* by George Shannon, illustrations by Laura Dronzek. Text copyright © 2003 by George W. B. Shannon. Illustrations copyright © 2003 by Laura Dronzek. Used by permission of HarperCollins Publishers.

Page 48: *Mole and the Baby Bird* by Marjorie Newman, illustrated by Patrick Benson. Text copyright © 2002 by Marjorie Newman. Illustrations copyright © 2002 by Patrick Benson. Reprinted by permission of Bloomsbury Publishing.

Page 80: Excerpt from *Dot & Jabber and the Great Acorn Mystery*, copyright © 2001 by Ellen Stoll Walsh, reprinted by permission of Harcourt, Inc. This material may not be reproduced in any form or by any means without the prior written permission of the publisher.

Page 114: From *Simple Machines* by Allan Fowler. © 2001 Children's Press®. A Division of Grolier Publishing Co., Inc. All rights reserved. Published simultaneously in Canada. Reprinted by permission.

Page 144: *Alexander Graham Bell* by Lola M. Schaefer. Copyright © 2003 by Capstone Press. Reprinted by permission.

Page 174: From *Ben Franklin and His First Kite*. Text copyright © 2002 by Stephen Krensky. Illustrations copyright © 2002 by Bert Dodson. Reprinted with permission of Aladdin Paperbacks, Simon & Schuster Children's Publishing Division. All rights reserved.

Page 198: "I Made A Mechanical Dragon" from *The Dragons are Singing Tonight* by Jack Prelutsky, illustrated by Peter Sis. Text copyright © 1993 by Jack Prelutsky. Illustrations copyright © 1993 by Peter Sis. Used by permission of HarperCollins Publishers.

Page 200: "Lighthouse" from *Flicker Flash*. Text copyright © 1999 by Joan Bransfield Graham. Illustrations copyright © 1999 by Nancy Davis. Reprinted by permission of Houghton Mifflin Company. All rights reserved.

Illustrations

Cover: Daniel Moreton

36-41 Viviana Garofoli

Photographs

Every effort has been made to secure permission and provide appropriate credit for photographic material. The publisher deeply regrets any omission and pledges to correct errors called to its attention in subsequent editions.

Unless otherwise acknowledged, all photographs are the property of Scott Foresman, a division of Pearson Education.

Photo locators denoted as follows: Top (T), Center (C), Bottom (B), Left (L), Right (R), Background (Bkgd).

7 ©Xavier Bonghi/Getty Images

8 (Bkgd) ©Klaus Hackenberg/zefa/Corbis, (L) ©Xavier Bonghi/Getty Images

10 ©Andy Roberts/Stone/Getty Images

11 (BL) Getty Images, (T) Ghislain & Marie David de Lossy/Image Bank/Getty Images

44 ©Martin Harvey/Gallo Images/Corbis

45 (TL, BL) AP/Wide World Photos, (CR) ©Chinch Gryniewicz/Ecoscene/Corbis

67 ©Carole Cutner/Walker Books Limited

103 ©Benjamin M. Walsh

110 ©Peter Samuels/Corbis

111 (B) ©Dennis MacDonald/PhotoEdit, (T) ©Royalty-Free/Corbis, (CR) ©Derek P. Redfearn/Getty Images

112 Getty Images

113 ©Comstock, Inc.

114 (CL) ©Comstock, Inc., (BC) Corbis

115 (Bkgd) ©Ross Whitaker/Getty Images, (BC) ©Comstock, Inc.

116 (CR) Corbis, (B) ©Comstock, Inc.

117 ©Nance S. Trueworthy

119 ©Tony Freeman/PhotoEdit

120 ©Michelle D. Bridwell/PhotoEdit

122 (TR) ©Royalty-Free/Corbis, (TL) ©Kayte M. Deioma/PhotoEdit, (B) ©Dennis MacDonald/PhotoEdit

123 Stock Boston

124 (T) ©David Young-Wolff/PhotoEdit, (B) ©Bonnie Kamin/PhotoEdit

125 ©David Forbert/SuperStock

126 Unicorn Stock Photos

127 (T) Affordable Photo Stock/Francis & Donna Caldwell, (B) ©Royalty-Free/Corbis

128 Stock Boston

129 (TL) ©Mary Kate Denny/PhotoEdit, (BR) ©Laurence Monneret/Getty Images

130 Stock Boston

131 (TL, BR) ©Tom Stewart/Corbis, (TR) ©Jennie Woodcock/Reflections Photolibrary/Corbis, (BL) ©George Shelley/Corbis

133 ©Comstock, Inc.

139 ©David Forbert/SuperStock

140 ©Royalty-Free/Corbis

141 (BL, TL) ©Bettmann/Corbis, (TR) Reuters/Corbis

142 ©Bettmann/Corbis

145 Corbis

147 ©E.O. Hoppe

149 ©A. G. Bell National Historic Site

Acknowledgments

Glossary

The contents of this glossary have been adapted from *First Dictionary*. Copyright © 2000, Pearson Education, Inc.